MEET ANDY CAPP

'E'S LUV'LY

Says Time Magazine:

He's a 5-ft. 4-in., 46-year-old, pot-bellied, wife-beating little lay-about. His floppy cap not only hides his eyes but never comes off — either in bed or on his rare visits to the tub. A cigarette is permanently glued to his lip. His bulbous nose glows whenever he has a snootful, which is nearly every night. He has no discernible trade and lives on the dole as if he had earned it. He is selfish, improvident, coarse, arrogant and bullying. "Don't stand out there in the cold, lass," he says to his sister-in-law, come to pay a visit. "Buzz off." His name is Andy Capp, and he is the newest folk hero of the comic strips...

[Artist Reginald] Smythe is as fond of Andy as Andy is of himself. After all, it was Artist Smythe who put these words in the mouths of Andy and Flo:

"C'mon, Andy, just for daft — say I'm luv'ly."

"Be'ave yerself, Flo. I'm gettin' embarrassed."

"Go on, say it just this once an' I'll never ask yer again."

"Oh, all right. I'm luv'ly."

— *Courtesy* TIME
© Copyright Time, Inc., 1963

Other ANDY CAPP Books in Fawcett Gold Medal Editions:

ANDY CAPP STRIKES BACK (abridged)	D1838
WHAT NEXT, ANDY CAPP?	D1845
HURRAY FOR ANDY CAPP	D1882
ANDY CAPP SOUNDS OFF	D1855
ANDY CAPP—MAN OF THE HOUR	D1859
IN YOUR EYE, ANDY CAPP	D1929
TAKE A BOW, ANDY CAPP	D1981
HATS OFF, ANDY CAPP	D2009

Only 50¢ Each—Wherever Paperbacks Are Sold

If your dealer is sold out, send cover price plus 10¢ each for postage and handling to Gold Medal Books, Fawcett Publications, Inc., Greenwich, Connecticut 06830. If order is for five or more books, there is no postage or handling charge. Order by number and title. No Canadian orders. Catalog available on request.

MEET ANDY CAPP

by Smythe

A FAWCETT GOLD MEDAL BOOK

Fawcett Publications, Inc., Greenwich, Conn.
Member of American Book Publishers Council, Inc.

A Fawcett Gold Medal Book published by arrangement with
The Hall Syndicate, Inc., and Daily Mirror, London.

Copyright © 1963, 1964 by The Hall Syndicate, Inc., and
Daily Mirror, London.

Copyright under International and Pan-American Copyright
Conventions. All rights reserved, including the right
to reproduce this book, or portions thereof, in any form.
All inquiries should be addressed to Hall House, Inc.,
262 Mason Street, Greenwich, Conn.

Library of Congress Catalog Number 64-15246

Printed in the United States of America

"Don't give me all that about yer bein' 'ard at work all day — this sofa's still warm!"

"I admit yours is gettin' the best of it — but mine's got better style."

"It's not that I don't love yer, Florrie. It's just that the
idea of a second honeymoon sickens me."

"Yer were in a disgustin' state last night, Chalkie —
yer dropped me twice on the way home."

"Remember now, I don't want to be invited back again — so just be yourself."

*"I 'ear Chalkie was in 'ere last night —
was I with 'im?"*

"Twenty years old, eh? — Bit small for its age, isn't it?"

"Not tonight, Mary, the doctor said not to drink so much — just gimme a double whisky."

"Now let's say you want to know the exact length of the River Ganges..."

"I can't bear to see yer strugglin' blindly with that lot, Florrie, lemme give yer a 'and."

"I never knew he drank until one night he came home sober."

"Yer never look at me like that!"

"I like to bring Florrie — it's the only bit of pleasure she gets."

"Yer don't know what this means to me, Andy, it's ages since we've done anythin' together!"

WHO'S 'AD ENOUGH? I'M NOT AS
THUNK AS YER DRINK I AM —

.... NOT AS. —

.... NOT AS THINK AS
YER DRUNK —

...YER RIGHT, LASS, TAKE ME 'OME

"All right then — I apologize!

*"Don't move! — Just lie there for a minute
an' let me drink yer in."*

"FLORRIE! Gimme the 'ammer!"

"Yer didn't get pins and needles when we were courtin'."

*"Yes yer did! — yer distinctly rustled yer paper
at me!"*

"No, no, you're next, sir — HE only comes in to read the papers."

"*I don't know who the little feller is, but it's his third time round.*"

"*Say good-night to Andy for us.*"

"I saw a good job advertised this mornin', so I went
round to see abaht it straight away —
yer start tomorrow."

"*What would I want wi' life insurance? She doesn't dare lay a finger on me.*"

"I don't know what's up wi' me, Doc . . . just can't seem to relax — I can't even sleep when we 'ave company."

"*Yer shiverin'! — I think I'd better put a spot of 'ot milk in yer rum.*"

"Good mornin'— could I 'ave a word with Eve?"

"I was only tryin' to be helpful."

"What a terrible thing to say to a dog!"

"*I kept tellin' Chalkie that I was takin' yer to the pictures, but 'e insisted on draggin' me in 'ere!*"

*"Sometimes I think he goes out of his way
to be obnoxious."*

"That's Mrs. Goodall's eldest. Grown up to be a fine-
lookin' lass, 'asn't she, Andy?"

"Yer imaginin' things, it was perfectly all right yesterday
when I touched up the pantry door with it."

"What exactly — in decent language — went wrong
with yer system, Andy?"

"*Between you an' me, I think that's why 'e wears 'is cap that way — e' can't bear to see a woman standin'.*"

"Of course *I've* thought about getting a job, what *IDIOT* hasn't!"

"They'll be 'ere any min — oh, for Pete's sake, Andy!
Chalkie and Rube are FRIENDS of ours!"

"I've got it going now, thank you . . . I said I've got it
going . . . I've — do you mind?"

"They 'ad somebody new be'ind the bar at the Crown tonight — pleasant kinda feller."

"'E's in a funny mood this mornin'."

SIX—
SEVEN—
EIGHT—

NINE—
TEN"

"Idle? *Me who spent weeks teachin' yer 'ow to mend a fuse, fix a washer, dig the garden —*"

"C'mon, lass, get up on yer feet, it's closin' time —"

"Andy an' me 'ave our differences of opinion, of course
— but I never tell 'im mine."

"It 'appened on me way 'ome last night, just as I was turnin' our corner some clumsy idiot trod on me fingers!"

BOP!

BAR

DON'T KID YERSELF, MATE — IT WAS THE FRESH AIR THAT KNOCKED ME OUT!